The Writer's Craft

Tests and Writing Assessment Prompts

Red Level
Grade 7

D1211043

McDougal Littell Inc.
A Houghton Mifflin Company
Evanston, Illinois   Boston Dallas Phoenix

College of the Ouachitas

ISBN 0-8123-8836-4

4 5 6 7 8 9 10 – MDO – 99 98 97

Contents

Writing Prompts

Grammar and Usage Pretests and Mastery Tests

Prompts for Personal and Expressive Writing

Wouldn't someone like to hear from you? Write a letter to a friend. In it, tell about something that happened to you recently. Tell about an incident that made you laugh—or brought tears to your eyes.

═══════

For a children's magazine, describe your first attempt at playing a particular sport. The sport might be one that looked easy but turned out to be a real challenge, or it might be one that came quite naturally to you. Be sure you tell what you did and how you felt about it.

═══════

What are some of the more important or interesting experiences you've had in your life? Have you moved, lost something that was important to you, or overcome a big fear? As you grow older, your memory of the events is bound to fade. So capture one of these experiences now in as much vivid detail as possible by writing a journal entry about it. Be sure to tell why the event was important to you.

═══════

Enter a magazine contest by writing an essay about somebody you admire. According to the contest rules, your hero should be a person that you know well or a historical figure—male or female, living or dead—that you've heard and read about. Tell how you feel about your hero, what qualities you admire, and the ways in which you would like your life to be like your hero's.

Prompts for Observation and Description

Have you seen a particularly skillful feat or performance by an athlete, a dancer, or an acrobat recently? Try to visualize the physical movements of the person, and write a description of the performance for the sports and entertainment section of your community newspaper. Use concrete details and imaginative comparisons to help your readers see and appreciate what you saw.

Is there a special object or a favorite tradition that is important to everyone in your family? For example, do you have an heirloom that has been handed down through generations, a quilt that your grandmother made, or a special way of celebrating birthdays? For a younger relative—perhaps even for someone who hasn't been born yet—describe this family treasure or tradition in as much detail as you can.

For an audience of your classmates, write a description of a particular time and place that you know well, such as your room on a rainy afternoon, the video arcade after school, or the waiting area at your doctor's office on a busy day. Use as many specific sensory details as you can. Try to capture the moment—and share how you feel about it.

For a class anthology, describe a bird, an insect, or an animal that you have strong feelings about. Choose one that scares, amuses, or puzzles you. Be sure you know enough about the animal to describe it fully. Use sensory details that will make your classmates feel the same

Prompts for Narrative and Literary Writing

Have you ever thought of just the right thing to say or do after an experience was over? Here is your chance to rewrite history. For your school literary magazine, write a narrative about something that happened to you—but make this story unfold just the way you wish it had in real life.

A younger relative has just learned that he wasn't chosen to be in his school's talent show. Disappointed, he has come to you for advice and support. What kind of story might you write to give him hope, comfort, or encouragement? You might think back over your own disappointments and successes. Then write a story based on one of these experiences to share with your relative.

The editors of your school literary magazine have decided to devote one entire issue to heroic adventures and daring rescues. Think about the rescues you have witnessed, participated in, or read about. Then write a story based on one of these rescues.

How would you like to be only two inches high or so tall that forests looked like clumps of broccoli? What would be some advantages of being so tiny or so huge? What would be some of the problems? Write a children's story about a person of unusual size. In your story, show how this character's size creates a problem or helps to solve one.

Prompts for Informative Writing: Explaining How

Are there any problems in your school? Do you get too little time to eat lunch? Between classes, is it hard to find a water fountain that works? In a letter, make your school principal aware of a school problem and suggest a solution. Be sure to explain what the causes of the problem are, who is affected by it, and how something could be done to solve it.

Your school is having a health awareness day. For the occasion, write a short composition about a health problem you think is avoidable. Begin with a brief explanation of the problem—how it comes about, who is affected by it, and how. Then tell how you think people could prevent this problem. In your conclusion, either urge your readers to follow your advice or warn them of what may happen if they don't.

Does somebody do something that really drives you crazy? Do you have a friend who always insists on being in charge? Is there someone in your class who always takes credit for other people's work? Choose something that bothers you. Now take a moment to figure out a way to resolve this problem. Then write a composition in which you describe the problem and explain your proposed solution to it. Address your composition to others who are also troubled by this behavior.

Think about some of the problems in your community that affect you and your friends. Choose a problem that concerns you. Then prepare a brief written report in which you state the problem, explain how it affects you, and offer a solution to it. In your report, make clear to your neighbors why they should do something about the problem.

Prompts for Informative Writing: Explaining What

Do you have a special relationship with someone? Take a moment now to consider why this person matters to you and what he or she adds to your life. Then write an essay in which you define the role of this individual in your life. You might begin with words like "An aunt is someone who . . . ." Plan to share this essay with the person about whom you're writing.

===

Most hobbies and sports have special words to describe the equipment and the plays unique to that activity. For example, chess players talk of *rooks* and *pawns,* and baseball players speak of *knuckleballs* and *sliders.* Imagine you are helping to write a manual for beginners in a hobby or sport you know well. Write an explanation of an important term that all beginners need to understand.

===

Choose a custom or holiday that you enjoy or that has special meaning for you. For instance, do you love celebrating Independence Day? Hanukah? Tet? In a letter to a pen pal, explain the practice or event you've chosen. As you write, remember that this pen pal lives in another country and knows nothing of your customs or holidays.

===

A magazine for teenagers is conducting a survey on teens' taste in movies. The editors want you to compare and contrast a movie that is in the theaters now with your favorite film of all time, and then draw a conclusion about what makes a movie great. The best responses will appear in a future issue of the magazine, so be sure to write for an audience of magazine readers your own age.

Prompts for Persuasion

Imagine that your school has had a full program of extracurricular activities. Now, however, tax cuts have made it necessary to cut all but one of these activities. Write a speech to be given at a public hearing of the school board in which you tell which program you think should be saved. Remember that to convince the board members you will need to support your opinion with reasons and specific examples.

What's your pet peeve? Is it graffiti? Too many television commercials? Violence in movies? Write an editorial for your school newspaper. Clearly state what your gripe is and what you think should be done about it. Try to persuade your readers to accept your opinion.

One student will have the chance to work at a local television studio this summer. This student will be expected to answer phones, run errands, and do some library research. Above all, however, this person needs to be responsible, reliable, and eager to learn. Write an essay to convince the station managers that you are the ideal person for the job. Include specific incidents and examples to support your statements.

Your class has decided to stage a mock trial. The defendant is the villain from one of your favorite fairy tales. The lawyer for the defense is you. Choose the villain you would like to represent. This might be the wolf in *Little Red Riding Hood,* the stepmother in *Cinderella,* or any other character. Then write down what you will say in your final remarks to the jury. In this speech, you need to convince the jury to find your defendant "not guilty." Therefore, be sure to support your points with facts and examples and to answer important objections to your views.

Understanding Sentences

Part 1 Identifying Parts of the Sentence
Choose the sentence that shows the complete subject and complete predicate correctly separated by a bar mark (|). (5 points each)

1. ○ A. An ambulance sped | to the scene of the accident.
   ○ B. An ambulance | sped to the scene of the accident.
   ○ C. An ambulance sped to the scene | of the accident.

2. ○ A. The four frightened kittens | hid under the porch.
   ○ B. The four | frightened kittens hid under the porch.
   ○ C. The four frightened kittens hid | under the porch.

3. ○ A. Greg | stirred the pudding for ten minutes.
   ○ B. Greg stirred the pudding | for ten minutes.
   ○ C. Greg stirred | the pudding for ten minutes.

Part 2 Recognizing Verbs and Their Subjects
Choose the answer that shows each simple subject underlined once and each verb underlined twice. (5 points each)

4. ○ A. Jack <u>had</u> the <u>measles</u> recently.
   ○ B. <u>Jack</u> had the <u>measles</u> recently.
   ○ C. <u>Jack</u> <u>had</u> the measles recently.

5. ○ A. From the <u>cave</u> <u>came</u> a shout.
   ○ B. From the cave <u>came</u> a <u>shout</u>.
   ○ C. From the <u>cave</u> came a <u>shout</u>.

6. ○ A. Did our <u>team</u> <u>win</u> the game?
   ○ B. <u>Did</u> our <u>team</u> win the game?
   ○ C. <u>Did</u> our <u>team</u> <u>win</u> the game?

7. ○ A. There <u>are</u> <u>plums</u> in the bowl.
   ○ B. There <u>are</u> plums in the bowl. (<u>You</u>)
   ○ C. <u>There</u> <u>are</u> plums in the bowl.

8. ○ A. <u>Mark</u> <u>is</u> becoming more self-confident.
   ○ B. <u>Mark</u> <u>is</u> <u>becoming</u> more self-confident.
   ○ C. <u>Mark</u> <u>is</u> becoming <u>more</u> self-confident.

9. ○ A. Today <u>Sue</u> <u>walked</u> to school with me.
   ○ B. Today Sue <u>walked</u> to school with <u>me</u>.
   ○ C. <u>Today</u> Sue <u>walked</u> to school with me.

Go to the next page.

10. ○ A. (You) <u>Hand</u> me that hammer.
   ○ B. (You) Hand me that <u>hammer</u>.
   ○ C. <u>Hand</u> <u>me</u> that hammer.

11. ○ A. The <u>boys</u> <u>had</u> <u>never</u> <u>seen</u> a copperhead.
   ○ B. The <u>boys</u> <u>had</u> <u>never</u> seen a copperhead.
   ○ C. The <u>boys</u> <u>had</u> never <u>seen</u> a copperhead.

12. ○ A. <u>Kim</u> <u>sat</u> by the <u>fireplace</u> and <u>read</u> a book.
   ○ B. <u>Kim</u> sat <u>by</u> the fireplace <u>and</u> read a book.
   ○ C. <u>Kim</u> <u>sat</u> by the fireplace and <u>read</u> a book.

13. ○ A. After the thaw, the <u>field</u> and the <u>park</u> <u>were</u> <u>soggy</u> and squishy.
   ○ B. After the <u>thaw</u>, the <u>field</u> and the park <u>were</u> soggy and squishy.
   ○ C. After the thaw, the <u>field</u> and the <u>park</u> <u>were</u> soggy and squishy.

Part 3 Recognizing Verbs
The simple predicate, or verb, has been underlined in each sentence below. Identify what kind of verb it is. (5 points each)

14. The tower <u>toppled</u> to the ground.
   ○ A. action verb   ○ B. state-of-being verb

15. The Leaning Tower of Pisa <u>is</u> famous.
   ○ A. state-of-being verb   ○ B. action verb

Part 4 Identifying Kinds of Sentences
Choose the answer that tells whether each sentence is *declarative, interrogative, imperative,* or *exclamatory.* (5 points each)

16. Are you superstitious
   ○ A. declarative   ○ B. interrogative   ○ C. imperative

17. What a gorgeous day this is
   ○ A. declarative   ○ B. exclamatory   ○ C. imperative

18. Join me on the volleyball team
   ○ A. interrogative   ○ B. exclamatory   ○ C. imperative

Part 5 Recognizing Sentence Fragments and Run-on Sentences
Choose the answer that tells whether each group of words is a *fragment, sentence,* or *run-on* sentence. (5 points each)

19. With wide eyes and a wider smile
   ○ A. fragment   ○ B. sentence   ○ C. run-on sentence

20. Wait for me I'm hurrying
   ○ A. fragment   ○ B. sentence   ○ C. run-on sentence

Understanding Sentences

Part 1 Identifying the Parts of a Sentence   Choose the sentence that shows the subject and predicate correctly separated by a bar mark (|). (4 points each)

1. ○ A. A black mare | raced along the backstretch.
   ○ B. A black mare raced | along the backstretch.
   ○ C. A black | mare raced along the backstretch.

2. ○ A. The fire | in the fireplace burned brightly.
   ○ B. The fire in the fireplace | burned brightly.
   ○ C. The fire in the fireplace burned | brightly.

3. ○ A. Several | cows grazed peacefully in the field.
   ○ B. Several cows grazed | peacefully in the field.
   ○ C. Several cows | grazed peacefully in the field.

4. ○ A. The twins deliver | newspapers after school.
   ○ B. The twins deliver newspapers | after school.
   ○ C. The twins | deliver newspapers after school.

Part 2 Identifying Simple Subjects and Their Verbs   Choose the answer that shows each subject underlined once and its verb underlined twice. (3 points each)

5. ○ A. The telephone on the <u>table</u> rang <u>suddenly</u>.
   ○ B. The <u>telephone</u> on the table <u>rang</u> suddenly.
   ○ C. The telephone on the <u>table</u> <u>rang</u> suddenly.

6. ○ A. This year Colin <u>wants</u> his own <u>guitar</u>.
   ○ B. This <u>year</u> Colin <u>wants</u> his own guitar.
   ○ C. This year <u>Colin</u> <u>wants</u> his own guitar.

7. ○ A. This morning <u>Ted</u> <u>gave</u> a speech in social studies class.
   ○ B. This morning Ted <u>gave</u> a <u>speech</u> in social studies class.
   ○ C. This morning Ted gave a speech in <u>social</u> <u>studies</u> <u>class</u>.

8. ○ A. <u>Tiny</u> <u>lights</u> flickered in the dark.
   ○ B. Tiny <u>lights</u> <u>flickered</u> in the dark.
   ○ C. Tiny lights <u>flickered</u> in the <u>dark</u>.

Part 3 Identifying Verbs   The simple predicate, or verb, has been underlined in each sentence below. Identify what kind of verb it is. (3 points each)

9. Clem <u>is</u> just my nickname.
   ○ A. action verb   ○ B. state-of-being verb

Go to the next page.

10. The models <u>looked</u> at themselves in the mirror.
   ○ A. action verb   ○ B. state-of-being verb

11. About 500 students <u>were</u> in the auditorium.
   ○ A. action verb   ○ B. state-of-being verb

Part 4 Identifying Main Verbs and Helping Verbs   Choose the answer
that shows the helping verb or verbs underlined once and the main verb
underlined twice. (3 points each)

12. ○ A. <u>Quinn</u> <u>is</u> sitting quietly in the kitchen.
   ○ B. Quinn <u>is</u> <u>sitting</u> quietly in the kitchen.
   ○ C. Quinn is <u>sitting</u> <u>quietly</u> in the kitchen.

13. ○ A. In Holland, tulips <u>do</u> <u>grow</u> everywhere.
   ○ B. In Holland, <u>tulips</u> do <u>grow</u> everywhere.
   ○ C. In Holland, tulips do <u>grow</u> <u>everywhere</u>.

14. ○ A. Alicia <u>did</u> <u>not</u> really want dessert.
   ○ B. Alicia <u>did</u> not really <u>want</u> dessert.
   ○ C. Alicia did not <u>really</u> <u>want</u> dessert.

15. ○ A. Amy <u>will</u> be <u>coming</u> home soon.
   ○ B. Amy <u>will</u> <u>be</u> <u>coming</u> home soon.
   ○ C. Amy will <u>be</u> <u>coming</u> <u>home</u> soon.

Part 5 Identifying Compound Subjects and Compound Verbs
Choose the sentence that shows the subject or subjects underlined once and
the verb or verbs underlined twice. (3 points each)

16. ○ A. The <u>weeds</u> and <u>insects</u> <u>invaded</u> the garden!
   ○ B. The <u>weeds</u> <u>and</u> insects <u>invaded</u> the garden!
   ○ C. The <u>weeds</u> and <u>insects</u> invaded the <u>garden</u>!

17. ○ A. <u>Nancy</u> <u>draws</u> and <u>paints</u> beautiful pictures.
   ○ B. <u>Nancy</u> <u>draws</u> and <u>paints</u> beautiful pictures.
   ○ C. <u>Nancy</u> <u>draws</u> and <u>paints</u> beautiful <u>pictures</u>.

18. ○ A. <u>Pepe</u> and his <u>father</u> <u>went</u> on a trip together.
   ○ B. Pepe and <u>his</u> <u>father</u> <u>went</u> on a trip together.
   ○ C. <u>Pepe</u> and his <u>father</u> went on a <u>trip</u> together.

19. ○ A. The <u>snow</u> <u>blew</u> and <u>drifted</u> across the ballpark.
   ○ B. The <u>snow</u> <u>blew</u> and <u>drifted</u> across the ballpark.
   ○ C. The snow <u>blew</u> and <u>drifted</u> across the <u>ballpark</u>.

Go to the next page.

Part 6 Identifying Kinds of Sentences
Choose the answer that tells whether each sentence is *declarative, interrogative, imperative,* or *exclamatory.* (3 points each)

20. What a terrific speech this is
    - ○ A. declarative
    - ○ B. interrogative
    - ○ C. imperative
    - ○ D. exclamatory

21. Turn left at the next stop light
    - ○ A. declarative
    - ○ B. interrogative
    - ○ C. imperative
    - ○ D. exclamatory

22. What time will you be here
    - ○ A. declarative
    - ○ B. interrogative
    - ○ C. imperative
    - ○ D. exclamatory

23. Snakes sometimes hibernate in logs
    - ○ A. declarative
    - ○ B. interrogative
    - ○ C. imperative
    - ○ D. exclamatory

Part 7 Identifying Subjects in Unusual Order
Choose the subject in each sentence. (2 points each)

24. Beyond the flat scrubland lies the ocean.
    - ○ A. Beyond
    - ○ B. ocean
    - ○ C. scrubland

25. After the speech came the refreshments.
    - ○ A. refreshments
    - ○ B. speech
    - ○ C. After

26. Just ahead of us was an oasis.
    - ○ A. ahead
    - ○ B. us
    - ○ C. oasis

Part 8 Identifying Subjects and Verbs in Questions, Exclamations, and Commands
Choose the answer that shows the subject underlined once and the verb underlined twice. (2 points each)

27.
    - ○ A. (You) Stop that!
    - ○ B. (You) Stop that!
    - ○ C. (You) Stop that!

28.
    - ○ A. Has the milk turned sour again?
    - ○ B. Has the milk turned sour again?
    - ○ C. Has the milk turned sour again?

Go to the next page.

29. ○ A. Were <u>we</u> <u>early</u> this morning!
○ B. <u>Were</u> <u>we</u> early this morning!
○ C. <u>Were</u> <u>we</u> <u>early</u> this morning!

Part 9 Using Sentences That Begin with *There*   Choose the answer that shows the subject underlined once and the verb underlined twice. (2 points each)

30. ○ A. There <u>is</u> a great art <u>museum</u> in Paris.
○ B. <u>There</u> <u>is</u> a great art museum in Paris.
○ C. There <u>is</u> a great art museum in <u>Paris</u>.

31. ○ A. <u>There</u> <u>were</u> letters for every camper.
○ B. There <u>were</u> <u>letters</u> for every camper.
○ C. <u>There</u> were <u>letters</u> for every camper.

32. ○ A. <u>Are</u> <u>there</u> other swamps in Florida besides the Okefenokee?
○ B. Are <u>there</u> other <u>swamps</u> in Florida besides the Okefenokee?
○ C. <u>Are</u> there other <u>swamps</u> in Florida besides the Okefenokee?

Part 10 Identifying Sentence Fragments and Run-on Sentences
Choose the answer that tells whether each group of words is a *fragment*, a *sentence,* or a *run-on sentence*. (3 points each)

33. We shopped at Macy's and had lunch in the cafeteria
○ A. fragment   ○ B. sentence   ○ C. run-on sentence

34. Every school in the district
○ A. fragment   ○ B. sentence   ○ C. run-on sentence

35. Luke believed in himself, many things were possible to him
○ A. fragment   ○ B. sentence   ○ C. run-on sentence

Using Nouns

Part 1 Identifying Nouns Choose the answer that includes all the nouns in each sentence. (5 points each)

1. The green caterpillar edged across the road.
- ○ A. green, caterpillar
- ○ B. caterpillar, road
- ○ C. edged, across
- ○ D. road

2. Did you mail my letter to San Diego?
- ○ A. mail, letter
- ○ B. letter, San Diego
- ○ C. you, mail
- ○ D. letter

3. The stormy gray clouds promised a blizzard.
- ○ A. stormy, gray
- ○ B. gray, clouds
- ○ C. clouds, blizzard
- ○ D. promised, blizzard

4. Success is very important to Herman.
- ○ A. Success, important
- ○ B. very, important, Herman
- ○ C. important
- ○ D. Success, Herman

Part 2 Using Nouns in Sentences Choose the answer that tells whether the underlined noun is used as a *subject*, a *direct object*, an *indirect object*, or a *predicate noun*. (5 points each)

5. Aunt Kay is my most interesting <u>relative</u>.
- ○ A. subject
- ○ B. direct object
- ○ C. indirect object
- ○ D. predicate noun

6. Pete offered <u>Tom</u> some free advice.
- ○ A. subject
- ○ B. direct object
- ○ C. indirect object
- ○ D. predicate noun

7. The frantic <u>passenger</u> closed his eyes and groaned.
- ○ A. subject
- ○ B. direct object
- ○ C. indirect object
- ○ D. predicate noun

8. Holly has the <u>talent</u> to become a ballet dancer.
- ○ A. subject
- ○ B. direct object
- ○ C. indirect object
- ○ D. predicate noun

9. Certainly <u>snails</u> must hibernate.
- ○ A. subject
- ○ B. direct object
- ○ C. indirect object
- ○ D. predicate noun

10. The clerk stamped my <u>ticket</u> once.
- A. subject
- B. direct object
- C. indirect object
- D. predicate noun

11. I sent <u>Tim</u> a picture of our mural.
- A. subject
- B. direct object
- C. indirect object
- D. predicate noun

12. With practice, Molly will be a good <u>shortstop</u>.
- A. subject
- B. direct object
- C. indirect object
- D. predicate noun

Part 3 Forming Plurals   Choose the correct plural of each noun. (5 points each)

13. mouse   ○ A. mouse   ○ B. mouses   ○ C. mice

14. sheep   ○ A. sheep   ○ B. sheeps   ○ C. sheepes

15. loss   ○ A. loss   ○ B. loses   ○ C. losses

16. calf   ○ A. calfs   ○ B. calves   ○ C. calfes

Part 4 Forming Possessives   Choose the correct possessive form of each underlined noun. (5 points each)

17. That is our <u>captain</u> idea.
- A. captains   ○ B. captains'   ○ C. captain's

18. The <u>team</u> photograph was in the newspaper.
- A. team'   ○ B. team's   ○ C. teams'

19. He is Mark <u>Jones</u> older brother.
- A. Jone's   ○ B. Jones'   ○ C. Jones's

20. The <u>children</u> reading room is on the first floor.
- A. children's   ○ B. childrens's   ○ C. childrens'

Using Nouns

Part 1 Identifying Nouns   In each set, choose the sentence that has all of the nouns underlined. (5 points each)

1. ○ A. The <u>snow</u> <u>swirled</u> across the highway during the <u>storm.</u>
   ○ B. The <u>snow</u> swirled across the <u>highway</u> during the <u>storm</u>.
   ○ C. The snow swirled <u>across</u> the <u>highway</u> <u>during</u> the storm.

2. ○ A. Grace softly hummed the <u>melody</u> for her <u>sister</u>.
   ○ B. <u>Grace</u> <u>softly</u> <u>hummed</u> the melody for her sister.
   ○ C. <u>Grace</u> softly hummed the <u>melody</u> for her <u>sister</u>.

3. ○ A. Do <u>babies</u> usually take <u>naps</u> in the <u>afternoon</u>?
   ○ B. Do <u>babies</u> usually take naps in the <u>afternoon</u>?
   ○ C. Do <u>babies</u> <u>usually</u> take naps in the afternoon?

Part 2 Identifying Proper Nouns and Common Nouns   Choose the answer that tells whether each underlined word is a *proper noun* or a *common noun*. The proper nouns have not been capitalized here. (5 points each)

4. Last <u>thanksgiving</u> we visited my grandparents.
   ○ A. proper   ○ B. common

5. We went fishing on the <u>mississippi</u> <u>river</u>.
   ○ A. proper   ○ B. common

6. Many schools have <u>computers</u>.
   ○ A. proper   ○ B. common

Part 3 Identifying Nouns Used as Subjects   Find the noun that is used as the subject of each sentence. (5 points each)

7. The old ferry takes cars across the bay.
   ○ A. ferry   ○ B. cars   ○ C. bay

8. Across the rocky creek waded the three girls.
   ○ A. rocky   ○ B. girls   ○ C. creek

Part 4 Identifying Nouns Used as Direct Objects   Choose the noun that is used as the direct object in each sentence. (5 points each)

9. The steel mill buys its coal from those mines.
   ○ A. mill   ○ B. mines   ○ C. coal

Go to the next page.

10. Please, Ken, don't wear that jacket to school.

    ○ A. Ken   ○ B. jacket   ○ C. school

Part 5 Identifying Nouns Used as Indirect Objects   Choose the noun that is used as the indirect object in each sentence. (5 points each)

11. Has Amy written her cousins a letter yet?

    ○ A. letter   ○ B. cousins   ○ C. Amy

12. A woman outside the store handed Bob a flyer.

    ○ A. Bob   ○ B. flyer   ○ C. store

Part 6 Identifying Predicate Nouns   Choose the noun that is used as a predicate noun in each sentence. (5 points each)

13. One good source of protein is yogurt.

    ○ A. yogurt   ○ B. protein   ○ C. source

14. Angela soon became a whiz at chess, too.

    ○ A. whiz   ○ B. chess   ○ C. too

Part 7 Forming the Plurals of Nouns   Choose the correct plural form of each noun. (5 points each)

15. potato   ○ A. potato   ○ B. potatos   ○ C. potatoes

16. jury   ○ A. jurys   ○ B. juries   ○ C. juryes

17. deer   ○ A. deer   ○ B. deers   ○ C. deeres

Part 8 Identifying the Correct Possessive Forms of Nouns   Choose the correct possessive form of each word. (5 points each)

18. James   ○ A. Jame's   ○ B. James's   ○ C. James'

19. foods   ○ A. foods'   ○ B. food's   ○ C. foods's

20. man   ○ A. mans'   ○ B. men'   ○ C. man's

Using Pronouns

Part 1 Substituting Pronouns for Nouns   Identify how the pronoun in each sentence is used. (4 points each)

1. Yesterday <u>we</u> saw paintings and drawings at the museum.
○ A. subject   ○ B. object   ○ C. possessive

2. Mr. Reeves lost <u>his</u> briefcase at the airport.
○ A. subject   ○ B. object   ○ C. possessive

3. During the first act, <u>they</u> noticed clues to the thief's identity.
○ A. subject   ○ B. object   ○ C. possessive

4. Todd brought his basketball and dribbled <u>it</u> in the schoolyard.
○ A. subject   ○ B. object   ○ C. possessive

Part 2 Choosing the Correct Pronoun   Choose the correct pronoun to complete each sentence. (4 points each)

5. Heidi checked out the library book because _____ was about her topic.
○ A. it   ○ B. they

6. Does the list include the Knotts and _____ ?
○ A. us   ○ B. we

7. _____ answers were different.
○ A. Their   ○ B. They're

8. _____ did the coach just send out?
○ A. Who   ○ B. Whom

9. Did the guide leave the map with _____ boys?
○ A. we   ○ B. us

10. _____ very hot weather for this time of year.
○ A. Its   ○ B. It's

11. I am going to buy _____ a new jacket.
○ A. myself   ○ B. me

12. _____ members of the band practice three days a week.
○ A. Us   ○ B. We

Go to the next page.

13. The Cougars and _____ are the newest teams in the league.
    ○ A. us   ○ B. we

14. Is this _____ beach bag, Hilary?
    ○ A. your   ○ B. you're

15. The guitarist in the red plaid shirt is _____.
    ○ A. him   ○ B. he

16. The noises startled Beverly and _____.
    ○ A. I   ○ B. me

Part 3 Finding Antecedents   Choose the correct antecedent for the underlined pronoun. (4 points each)

17. The class listened as Ted explained <u>his</u> project to Anne.
    ○ A. class   ○ B. Ted   ○ C. project

18. Robert asked John why <u>he</u> left the party so early.
    ○ A. John   ○ B. Robert   ○ C. party

19. Every fall, a crew drains the pool and covers <u>it</u> with plastic.
    ○ A. fall   ○ B. crew   ○ C. pool

Choose the correct pronoun for each sentence. (4 points each)

20. Maria or Elena will start _____ piano lessons tomorrow.
    ○ A. their   ○ B. her

21. Two cardinals perched on a vine and pulled twigs for _____ nest.
    ○ A. their   ○ B. its

22. All the winners received _____ trophies at the ceremony.
    ○ A. his   ○ B. their

23. Ask David and Jack whether _____ would like to join us.
    ○ A. they   ○ B. he

24. Each of the swimmers splashed water at _____ friends.
    ○ A. their   ○ B. her

25. Neither of the neighbors added _____ name to the list.
    ○ A. them   ○ B. his

Using Pronouns

Part 1 Substituting Pronouns for Nouns Identify how the underlined pronoun in each sentence is used. (2 points each)

1. Jack and I are best friends.
○ A. subject   ○ B. object   ○ C. possessive

2. Did Lydia give him the new rehearsal schedule?
○ A. subject   ○ B. object   ○ C. possessive

3. Skiers left their tracks all over the fresh snow.
○ A. subject   ○ B. object   ○ C. possessive

4. After losing my ring, I looked for it in my locker.
○ A. subject   ○ B. object   ○ C. possessive

5. The Garcias visited her on Wednesday.
○ A. subject   ○ B. object   ○ C. possessive

6. That book is definitely his.
○ A. subject   ○ B. object   ○ C. possessive

7. Mr. Koh gave free tickets to Larry and me.
○ A. subject   ○ B. object   ○ C. possessive

8. We MacGillicuddys always stick together.
○ A. subject   ○ B. object   ○ C. possessive

Part 2 Using Subject and Object Pronouns Choose the correct pronoun form for each blank. (2 points each)

9. _____ did you invite to the party?
○ A. Whom   ○ B. Who

10. Let's keep this between you and _____.
○ A. I   ○ B. me

11. Mrs. Warren offered Janine and _____ a ride.
○ A. she   ○ B. her

12. That is _____ in the middle of the picture.
○ A. him   ○ B. he

13. The detective asked both Lauren and _____ many questions.
○ A. them   ○ B. they

Go to the next page.

14. _____ and John attended a sports camp.
○ A. Him   ○ B. He

15. The Zollmans and _____ are co-owners.
○ A. them   ○ B. they

16. The most surprised winners were _____.
○ A. they   ○ B. them

17. _____ referees are human too.
○ A. Us   ○ B. We

18. _____ is your teacher this year?
○ A. Who   ○ B. Whom

19. The florist sold Meg and _____ a basket of wildflowers.
○ A. I   ○ B. me

20. He met Juan and _____ at the airport.
○ A. her   ○ B. she

21. Give the message to _____ and his friend.
○ A. he   ○ B. him

22. The best judges are _____ two.
○ A. we   ○ B. us

Part 3 Using Possessive Pronouns   Choose the correct pronoun or contraction. (2 points each)

23. The park has lost _____ appeal for me.
○ A. its   ○ B. it's

24. Do you know whether _____ going?
○ A. they're   ○ B. their

25. _____ house is in Fairbanks, Alaska.
○ A. They're   ○ B. Their

26. Is _____ mother or father at home?
○ A. your   ○ B. you're

Go to the next page.

27. _____ hard for me to explain.
   ○ A. Its   ○ B. It's

28. Can you give me _____ word on that?
   ○ A. your   ○ B. you're

Part 4 Using Reflexive and Intensive Pronouns   Identify the use of
the underlined pronoun in each sentence. (2 points)

29. Hector did <u>himself</u> a favor by agreeing to help.
   ○ A. reflexive   ○ B. intensive

30. The boys prepared the meal <u>themselves</u>.
   ○ A. reflexive   ○ B. intensive

31. Let's give <u>ourselves</u> a little pat on the back!
   ○ A. reflexive   ○ B. intensive

32. Ana hummed softly to <u>herself</u>.
   ○ A. reflexive   ○ B. intensive

33. I <u>myself</u> do not like chocolate very much.
   ○ A. reflexive   ○ B. intensive

Part 5 Recognizing Pronouns and Their Antecedents and Making
Them Agree   In each sentence, find a pronoun with an antecedent, and
identify both words. (2 points each)

34. The tall boy in front of Kevin is blocking his view.
   ○ A. his, boy   ○ B. his, Kevin

35. A guinea pig must sometimes have its nails clipped.
   ○ A. its, nails   ○ B. its, guinea pig

36. Students with gold stars next to their names are semifinalists.
   ○ A. their, names   ○ B. their, Students

37. Ivan reached toward Doug to shake his hand.
   ○ A. his, Ivan   ○ B. his, Doug

38. Janet gave Ms. Ellison her solemn promise.
   ○ A. her, Janet   ○ B. her, Ms. Ellison

39. The car stood in the driveway with its motor running.
   ○ A. its, car   ○ B. its, driveway

Go to the next page.

Choose the correct pronoun form for each sentence. (2 points each)

40. The orchestra and the chorus put on _____ spring concert.
○ A. its   ○ B. their

41. Of the three, only Ben finished _____ assignment.
○ A. his   ○ B. their

42. Gina and Mary earned _____ allowances.
○ A. her   ○ B. their

43. A large cloud moved slowly, casting _____ shadow on the ground below.
○ A. its   ○ B. their

44. The owner of the lost gloves also lost _____ ticket.
○ A. his   ○ B. their

Part 6 Using Indefinite Pronouns   Choose the correct pronoun.
(2 points each)

45. Everybody sold _____ quota of tickets.
○ A. his or her   ○ B. their

46. Each of the campers must carry _____ own equipment.
○ A. her   ○ B. their

47. Several of the old books had _____ original covers.
○ A. its   ○ B. their

48. Someone left _____ sweater on that chair.
○ A. her   ○ B. their

49. All of the members of the club have paid _____ dues.
○ A. his or her   ○ B. their

50. Neither of the boys finished _____ lunch.
○ A. his   ○ B. their

Using Verbs

Part 1 Identifying Verbs, Objects, and Predicate Words   Identify the answer that correctly describes the underlined word in each sentence. (4 points each)

1. Randall's freckles <u>became</u> darker over the summer.
   ○ A. action verb   ○ B. linking verb

2. Save a <u>seat</u> for me at the assembly.
   ○ A. direct object   ○ B. predicate word

3. The lifeguard <u>shouted</u> at the swimmer.
   ○ A. transitive verb   ○ B. intransitive verb

4. Ben's closet <u>was</u> a disaster area!
   ○ A. action verb   ○ B. linking verb

5. After several weeks of practice, Jill became very <u>good</u> at chess.
   ○ A. predicate word   ○ B. direct object

6. The No. 41 bus <u>goes</u> to the zoo.
   ○ A. present tense   ○ B. present perfect tense

7. Pat <u>wore</u> his new jacket everywhere for a while.
   ○ A. action verb   ○ B. linking verb

8. Did Sandy lose her <u>place</u> on the debating team?
   ○ A. predicate word   ○ B. direct object

9. Mrs. Higgins <u>listed</u> her friends' names in a notebook.
   ○ A. transitive verb   ○ B. intransitive verb

10. According to the forecast, the snow <u>will stop</u> by tonight.
    ○ A. present tense   ○ B. future tense

11. Around midnight the storm finally <u>began</u>.
    ○ A. transitive verb   ○ B. intransitive verb

12. A Sikorsky flying crane delivered the heavy <u>equipment</u>.
    ○ A. direct object   ○ B. predicate word

13. Jacqueline felt the cool <u>air</u>.
    ○ A. predicate word   ○ B. direct object

Go to the next page.

14. That bicycle tire looks <u>flat</u> to me.
   ○ A. predicate word   ○ B. direct object

15. Laura <u>had</u> <u>finished</u> all her chores by noon.
   ○ A. past tense   ○ B. past perfect tense

Part 2 Identifying Verb Phrases   Identify the answer that shows each helping verb underlined once and each main verb underlined twice. (4 points each)

16. ○ A. The computer <u>can</u> <u>probably</u> <u>answer</u> your question.
   ○ B. The computer <u>can</u> <u>probably</u> answer your question.
   ○ C. The computer <u>can</u> probably <u>answer</u> your question.

17. ○ A. Sean has <u>been</u> <u>typing</u> for the last hour.
   ○ B. Sean <u>has</u> <u>been</u> <u>typing</u> for the last hour.
   ○ C. Sean <u>has</u> <u>been</u> typing for the last hour.

18. ○ A. I <u>must</u> not <u>have</u> <u>understood</u> the directions.
   ○ B. I <u>must</u> <u>not</u> <u>have</u> <u>understood</u> the directions.
   ○ C. I <u>must</u> <u>not</u> <u>have</u> <u>understood</u> the directions.

Part 3 Using Correct Verbs and Verb Parts   Choose the correct word to go in each blank. (4 points each)

19. Dan _____ a jackknife into the pool.
   ○ A. did   ○ B. done

20. The ground has been _____ since last Saturday's race.
   ○ A. froze   ○ B. frozen

21. Lee has _____ to the library.
   ○ A. went   ○ B. gone

22. Have you ever _____ to learn another language?
   ○ A. tryed   ○ B. tried

23. Please _____ me ride your bike.
   ○ A. leave   ○ B. let

24. The cat is _____ on the windowsill.
   ○ A. lying   ○ B. laying

25. I _____ my lunchbox under a shady tree.
   ○ A. set   ○ B. sat

Using Verbs

Part 1 Identifying Action and Linking Verbs   Identify the answer that tells whether each underlined verb is an action verb or a linking verb. (5 points each)

1. Marcie <u>brushed</u> her dog's hair.
   ○ A. action   ○ B. linking

2. Before the storm, the sky <u>became</u> very dark.
   ○ A. action   ○ B. linking

Part 2 Selecting Direct Objects   Identify the direct object in each sentence. (5 points each)

3. Vivian won the game with her ninth-inning homer.
   ○ A. Vivian   ○ B. won   ○ C. game   ○ D. homer

4. Charlie added blueberries to the pancake batter.
   ○ A. batter   ○ B. blueberries   ○ C. pancake   ○ D. Charlie

Part 3 Identifying Transitive and Intransitive Verbs   Identify the answer that tells whether each underlined verb is transitive or intransitive. (5 points each)

5. The snow <u>stuck</u> to the trees and bushes.
   ○ A. transitive   ○ B. intransitive

6. Water <u>covered</u> every inch of the basement floor.
   ○ A. transitive   ○ B. intransitive

7. Natalie usually <u>sits</u> behind Gwen in class.
   ○ A. transitive   ○ B. intransitive

Part 4 Recognizing Linking Verbs and Predicate Words   Identify the answer that shows the linking verb underlined once and the predicate word underlined twice. (5 points each)

8. ○ A. The flavor of the soup <u>was</u> <u>most</u> unusual.
   ○ B. The flavor of the soup <u>was</u> most <u>unusual</u>.
   ○ C. The flavor of the <u>soup</u> <u>was</u> most unusual.

9. ○ A. Milly <u>became</u> <u>better</u> at soccer.
   ○ B. Milly <u>became</u> better at <u>soccer</u>.
   ○ C. Milly <u>became</u> <u>better</u> at soccer.

Part 5 Identifying Verb Phrases Identify the answer that shows the helping verb underlined once and the main verb underlined twice. (5 points each)

10. ○ A. Have you <u>eaten</u> breakfast <u>yet</u>?
    ○ B. Have you <u>eaten</u> <u>breakfast</u> yet?
    ○ C. <u>Have</u> you <u>eaten</u> breakfast yet?

11. ○ A. Gene <u>could</u> <u>not</u> <u>fit</u> everything into his bag.
    ○ B. Gene <u>could</u> not <u>fit</u> everything into his bag.
    ○ C. Gene <u>could</u> <u>not</u> <u>fit</u> everything into his bag.

Part 6 Identifying Verb Tenses Identify the answer that tells what verb tense is used in each sentence. (5 points each)

12. Donovan skated around the rink.
    ○ A. present   ○ B. past   ○ C. future

13. I have not thought about it.
    ○ A. present   ○ B. past   ○ C. present perfect

14. Those pegs will not fit the chair legs.
    ○ A. present   ○ B. past perfect   ○ C. future

Part 7 Using the Principal Parts of Verbs Choose the correct verb part. (5 points each)

15. You have _____ notes in the book.
    ○ A. wrote   ○ B. written

16. The river _____ its banks.
    ○ A. overflew   ○ B. overflowed

17. Have we _____ all the cold chicken?
    ○ A. ate   ○ B. eaten

Part 8 Using the Right Verb Choose the correct verb. (5 points each)

18. Danny was _____ in the last row.
    ○ A. sitting   ○ B. setting

19. I had _____ my gloves on the radiator.
    ○ A. lain   ○ B. laid

20. The coach will _____ Tara stay on the team.
    ○ A. leave   ○ B. let

Using Adjectives

Part 1 Identifying Adjectives   Identify the adjective in each sentence.
(5 points each)

1. Nectarines are sweeter than oranges.
   ○ A. Nectarines   ○ B. sweeter   ○ C. than   ○ D. oranges

2. More people are participating in triathlons than ever before.
   ○ A. More   ○ B. people   ○ C. participating   ○ D. triathlons

3. Does everyone here like Chinese food?
   ○ A. everyone   ○ B. like   ○ C. Chinese   ○ D. food

4. Peaches and fresh cream were served.
   ○ A. Peaches   ○ B. fresh   ○ C. cream   ○ D. served

Part 2 Identifying Words Modified by Adjectives   Identify the noun
that is modified by the adjective underlined in each sentence. (5 points each)

5. This coat is the <u>warmest</u> of the three at this price.
   ○ A. This   ○ B. coat   ○ C. three

6. Sharon is <u>taller</u> than Cynthia.
   ○ A. Sharon   ○ B. than   ○ C. Cynthia

7. The buildings in the distance look <u>bluish-gray</u> against the sky.
   ○ A. buildings   ○ B. distance   ○ C. sky

8. The lake looks <u>cleaner</u> today than usual.
   ○ A. usual   ○ B. lake   ○ C. looks

Part 3 Using Adjectives to Compare   Choose the correct form of each
adjective to complete each sentence. (5 points each)

9. Zeke has the _____ average of the two semifinalists.
   ○ A. better   ○ B. more better   ○ C. best

10. According to the chart, Mont Blanc is the _____ peak in the Alps.
    ○ A. higher   ○ B. highest   ○ C. most high

11. Saint Augustine is the _____ city in the United States.
    ○ A. older   ○ B. oldest   ○ C. most old

12. This brand tastes better than that one, but it is also _____.
    ○ A. more expensive   ○ B. expensiver   ○ C. most expensive

Go to the next page.

Part 4 Identifying Types of Adjectives   Choose the answer that describes the underlined word in each sentence. (5 points each)

13. Did <u>those</u> letters on the table arrive today?
   - ○ A. possessive pronoun used as subject
   - ○ B. possessive pronoun used as adjective
   - ○ C. demonstrative adjective
   - ○ D. demonstrative pronoun

14. We never use <u>our</u> toaster any more.
   - ○ A. possessive pronoun used as subject
   - ○ B. possessive pronoun used as adjective
   - ○ C. demonstrative adjective
   - ○ D. demonstrative pronoun

15. I have my book bag, but <u>your</u> bag is lost.
   - ○ A. predicate adjective
   - ○ B. possessive pronoun used as adjective
   - ○ C. demonstrative adjective
   - ○ D. demonstrative pronoun

16. <u>This</u> sand is too hot to walk on with bare feet.
   - ○ A. possessive pronoun used as subject
   - ○ B. possessive pronoun used as adjective
   - ○ C. demonstrative adjective
   - ○ D. demonstrative pronoun

17. After all my reminders, <u>his</u> coat is still on my chair.
   - ○ A. possessive pronoun used as subject
   - ○ B. possessive pronoun used as adjective
   - ○ C. demonstrative adjective
   - ○ D. demonstrative pronoun

18. We bought <u>this</u> clock at Nagle's Department Store.
   - ○ A. possessive pronoun used as object
   - ○ B. possessive pronoun used as adjective
   - ○ C. demonstrative adjective
   - ○ D. demonstrative pronoun

19. Where did Tim leave <u>his</u> hammer?
   - ○ A. possessive pronoun used as object
   - ○ B. possessive pronoun used as adjective
   - ○ C. demonstrative adjective
   - ○ D. demonstrative pronoun

20. Please hand me <u>the</u> towel.
   - ○ A. possessive pronoun used as adjective
   - ○ B. indefinite article
   - ○ C. definite article
   - ○ D. demonstrative adjective

Using Adjectives

Part 1 Identifying Adjectives   Identify the word group that has an adjective and the word that the adjective modifies in the sentence. (4 points each)

1. After my accident, my old bicycle needed new brakes.
○ A. old, bicycle   ○ B. my, old   ○ C. new, needed

2. For several anxious minutes, nobody heard a single sound.
○ A. several, anxious   ○ B. several, minutes   ○ C. nobody, heard

3. Jackson mumbled a few words and quickly left the stage.
○ A. mumbled, few   ○ B. few, words   ○ C. quickly, left

4. The Australian team placed second in the relay.
○ A. second, placed   ○ B. The, Australian   ○ C. Australian, team

5. The valuable antique was sold at auction.
○ A. The, valuable   ○ B. The, antique   ○ C. at, auction

Part 2 Finding Predicate Adjectives   Identify the predicate adjective. (4 points each)

6. The silk flowers looked real to the casual observer.
○ A. silk   ○ B. real   ○ C. casual

7. All of these numbers on this chart are even.
○ A. All   ○ B. this   ○ C. even

8. Everyone in my family felt sleepy after the big dinner.
○ A. my   ○ B. sleepy   ○ C. big

9. The chimps in the largest cage were playful.
○ A. largest   ○ B. cage   ○ C. playful

10. Anita seems very proud of her trophy.
○ A. very   ○ B. proud   ○ C. her

Part 3 Using Adjectives to Compare   Choose the correct adjective form. (4 points each)

11. I attend one of the _____ high schools in the country.
○ A. biggest   ○ B. most big   ○ C. most biggest

12. This racer is the _____ of the three bicycles.
○ A. faster   ○ B. most fast   ○ C. fastest

Go to the next page.

College of the Ouachitas

13. Scrubbing the wall made an even _____ mess than we had before.
   ○ A. worst   ○ B. worse   ○ C. worser

14. That is the _____ pizza place of the four in town.
   ○ A. goodest   ○ B. better   ○ C. best

15. Your argument is the _____ one that I have ever heard.
   ○ A. foolishest   ○ B. most foolish   ○ C. more foolish

16. Nels is the _____ student in the seventh grade.
   ○ A. more young   ○ B. most young   ○ C. youngest

Part 4 Identifying Possessive Pronouns Used as Adjectives

Identify the possessive pronoun that is used as an adjective in each sentence. (4 points each)

17. I will look through my notebook again for those history notes.
   ○ A. I   ○ B. my   ○ C. those

18. You may pick up your new glasses today.
   ○ A. You   ○ B. up   ○ C. your

19. We bought our denim jackets at the discount store.
   ○ A. We   ○ B. our   ○ C. the

20. Those new students don't know their schedules yet.
   ○ A. Those   ○ B. new   ○ C. their

Part 5 Identifying Demonstrative Adjectives and Demonstrative Pronouns

Decide whether each underlined word is a demonstrative adjective or a demonstrative pronoun. (4 points each)

21. Heather gave me this bracelet for my birthday.
   ○ A. demonstrative adjective   ○ B. demonstrative pronoun

22. Are these the only mittens on sale?
   ○ A. demonstrative adjective   ○ B. demonstrative pronoun

Choose the best word or phrase to complete each sentence. (4 points each)

23. The cafeteria rarely serves _____ kinds of foods.
   ○ A. that   ○ B. those   ○ C. those there

24. Strangely enough, _____ sort of wasp is called a velvet ant.
   ○ A. these   ○ B. this here   ○ C. this

25. Don't _____ kinds of reptiles need live food?
   ○ A. these   ○ B. this   ○ C. these here

Using Adverbs

Part 1 Identifying Adverbs Find the adverb or adverbs in each sentence. (4 points each)

1. The tournament started early.
- ○ A. tournament
- ○ B. started, early
- ○ C. early
- ○ D. tournament, started

2. Outside, it was quite cool.
- ○ A. Outside, quite
- ○ B. quite, cool
- ○ C. was, quite
- ○ D. Outside, cool

3. Suddenly, a heavy rain came down.
- ○ A. Suddenly, rain
- ○ B. came, down
- ○ C. Suddenly, down
- ○ D. Suddenly, heavy

4. Herb felt very happy.
- ○ A. felt, very
- ○ B. very
- ○ C. happy
- ○ D. felt, happy

5. I have never heard that song before.
- ○ A. never
- ○ B. heard, that
- ○ C. never, heard
- ○ D. never, before

Identify the word that is modified by each underlined adverb. (4 points each)

6. May we leave <u>early</u> for the picnic?
- ○ A. we
- ○ B. leave
- ○ C. picnic

7. You seemed <u>barely</u> awake during the movie.
- ○ A. You
- ○ B. seemed
- ○ C. awake

8. Mel <u>often</u> practices karate.
- ○ A. Mel
- ○ B. practices
- ○ C. karate

9. Molasses pours <u>extremely</u> slowly out of the bottle.
- ○ A. slowly
- ○ B. pours
- ○ C. Molasses

10. <u>Today</u> I met my favorite hockey player.
- ○ A. met
- ○ B. favorite
- ○ C. player

Go to the next page.

Part 2 Using Adverbs Correctly   Choose the correct adverb to complete each sentence. (4 points each)

11. You played _____ in the last game.
○ A. good   ○ B. well

12. Chimps grow _____ than humans.
○ A. more quickly   ○ B. more quicker

13. Jeff sang _____ of all the members of the choir.
○ A. loudest   ○ B. loudliest

14. We climbed _____ over the rocks.
○ A. careful   ○ B. carefully

15. No one prints _____ than Cindy.
○ A. best   ○ B. better

16. Brian takes disappointments _____.
○ A. well   ○ B. good

17. Harold drives _____ than his brother.
○ A. more carefully   ○ B. more careful

18. When the other team laughed at us, we got _____ angry.
○ A. really   ○ B. real

19. As time for the test ran out, I answered the questions _____ than before.
○ A. recklesslier   ○ B. more recklessly

20. She swung _____ at the ball.
○ A. wild   ○ B. wildly

Part 3 Using Negatives Correctly   Choose the correct word to complete each sentence. (4 points each)

21. It _____ no warmer today than it was yesterday.
○ A. is   ○ B. isn't

22. I don't want any kumquats _____.
○ A. neither   ○ B. either

23. Nadine wasn't eating _____ of her carrots.
○ A. any   ○ B. none

24. Linda hasn't _____ won a prize.
○ A. never   ○ B. ever

25. I don't have _____ construction paper for the art project.
○ A. any   ○ B. no

Using Adverbs

Part 1 Identifying Adverbs   Identify the adverb or adverbs in each sentence. (5 points each)

1. He stuck stubbornly to his story.
- ○ A. He
- ○ B. stuck, stubbornly
- ○ C. stubbornly
- ○ D. stuck, to

2. In this light, your hair looks almost black.
- ○ A. almost
- ○ B. this, almost
- ○ C. black
- ○ D. almost, black

3. The sprinters ran very quickly.
- ○ A. sprinters, quickly
- ○ B. very, quickly
- ○ C. ran, very
- ○ D. quickly

4. Tonight Ryan will baby-sit for the first time.
- ○ A. Tonight
- ○ B. baby-sit, first
- ○ C. first
- ○ D. for, first

5. Miriam heard a scratchy noise overhead.
- ○ A. scratchy
- ○ B. noise
- ○ C. scratchy, overhead
- ○ D. overhead

Identify the word that is modified by each underlined adverb. (5 points each)

6. The shortstop limped <u>painfully</u> on his left foot.
- ○ A. limped
- ○ B. shortstop
- ○ C. left

7. King George was <u>very</u> confident of victory.
- ○ A. was
- ○ B. confident
- ○ C. victory

8. The old turtle moved <u>quite</u> slowly.
- ○ A. old
- ○ B. moved
- ○ C. slowly

9. I left my muddy boots <u>outside</u>.
- ○ A. muddy
- ○ B. left
- ○ C. boots

Part 2 Using Adverbs in Comparisons   Choose the correct word or words to complete each sentence. (5 points each)

10. Alex had never stayed awake _____ than midnight
- ○ A. later
- ○ B. more lately

Go to the next page.

11. Josh talked the _____ of anyone.
○ A. lesser ○ B. least

12. The car seats four _____ than five.
○ A. more comfortable ○ B. more comfortably

13. Of the four girls, Cynthia pitches _____.
○ A. best ○ B. better

Part 3 Distinguishing Between Adjectives and Adverbs Choose
the correct word to complete each sentence. (5 points each)

14. Michelle plays the banjo _____.
○ A. good ○ B. well

15. The weather changes _____ in the spring.
○ A. suddenly ○ B. sudden

16. At this school, everyone is _____ friendly.
○ A. real ○ B. really

17. The suitcase was _____ heavy.
○ A. awful ○ B. awfully

Part 4 Using Negatives Correctly Choose the correct word to complete
each sentence. (5 points each)

18. I couldn't train the dog, _____.
○ A. either ○ B. neither

19. It wasn't _____ trouble at all.
○ A. no ○ B. any

20. Julie never carries _____ money.
○ A. any ○ B. no

Using Prepositions, Conjunctions, and Interjections

Part 1 Identifying Prepositions   Find the prepositions in each sentence. (4 points each)

1. Water flowed noisily over the dam.
   ○ A. flowed   ○ B. over   ○ C. noisily

2. The damage occurred later below ground.
   ○ A. later   ○ B. below   ○ C. ground

3. The bear visited the camp again during a rainstorm.
   ○ A. The   ○ B. again   ○ C. during

4. Saul leaned back against a wall.
   ○ A. leaned   ○ B. against   ○ C. back

5. Often Jim rested between innings.
   ○ A. Often   ○ B. rested   ○ C. between

6. A flock of seagulls followed the fishing boat.
   ○ A. followed   ○ B. of   ○ C. flock

7. The sign in the window fell down.
   ○ A. in   ○ B. fell   ○ C. down

8. Without warning, the storm struck the valley.
   ○ A. Without   ○ B. valley   ○ C. struck

9. The mouse ran underneath the sofa.
   ○ A. mouse   ○ B. underneath   ○ C. sofa

Part 2 Identifying Prepositional Phrases   Identify the prepositional phrase in each sentence. (4 points each)

10. Someone had fallen through the ice.
   ○ A. had fallen   ○ B. fallen through   ○ C. through the ice

11. The man with the red cane is my father.
   ○ A. The man   ○ B. with the red cane   ○ C. my father

12. The mysterious travelers stopped at the inn.
   ○ A. mysterious travelers   ○ B. at the inn   ○ C. the inn

13. The woman in the blue coat lost her ring not far away.
   ○ A. lost her ring   ○ B. in the blue coat   ○ C. not far away

Go to the next page.

Part 3 Using Pronouns as Objects of Prepositions   Choose the
correct word to complete the sentence. (4 points each)

14. Kirk asked for any mail addressed to _____.
   ○ A. he   ○ B. him

15. The roof above Reynaldo and _____ was leaking.
   ○ A. her   ○ B. she

16. On the pavement, Lila drew a circle around Jackie and _____.
   ○ A. me   ○ B. I

17. From _____ did you receive the flowers?
   ○ A. who   ○ B. whom

Part 4 Identifying Adjective and Adverb Phrases   Identify each
underlined phrase as an adjective phrase or an adverb phrase. (4 points each)

18. The owner of the dog called me.
   ○ A. adjective phrase   ○ B. adverb phrase

19. On the letter was a red stamp.
   ○ A. adjective phrase   ○ B. adverb phrase

20. I prefer the oranges with thin skin.
   ○ A. adjective phrase   ○ B. adverb phrase

21. Jan and Jerry hiked for four hours.
   ○ A. adjective phrase   ○ B. adverb phrase

Part 5 Recognizing Conjunctions and Interjections   Identify the
conjunction or interjection in each sentence. (4 points each)

22. The weather forecast called for sleet or snow.
   ○ A. The   ○ B. for   ○ C. or

23. The men lifted the load into the truck slowly but surely.
   ○ A. into   ○ B. slowly   ○ C. but

24. Yippee! Willie Anton won the race.
   ○ A. Yippee   ○ B. won   ○ C. the

25. In the afternoon, the farmers will plow and seed the large field.
   ○ A. In   ○ B. and   ○ C. seed

Using Prepositions, Conjunctions, and Interjections

Part 1 Identifying Prepositions   Find the prepositions in each sentence. (4 points each)

1. The mechanic checked underneath the car for a broken muffler.
   ○ A. the, for   ○ B. underneath, for   ○ C. underneath, car

2. The package beside the radio was delivered to the wrong house.
   ○ A. beside, to   ○ B. was, house   ○ C. beside, radio

3. A cloud of smoke hung over the town and the surrounding fields.
   ○ A. over, surrounding ○ B. of, and   ○ C. of, over

4. No train has passed through the tunnel during the morning.
   ○ A. no, during   ○ B. through, the   ○ C. through, during

5. Along the river, willow trees trembled in the breeze.
   ○ A. the, river   ○ B. in, breeze   ○ C. Along, in

Identify each underlined word as a preposition or an adverb. (4 points each)

6. Before long, the containers filled <u>up</u> with water.
   ○ A. preposition   ○ B. adverb

7. His action goes far <u>beyond</u> the call of duty.
   ○ A. preposition   ○ B. adverb

8. Eventually, two of the boats fell <u>behind</u> the leader.
   ○ A. preposition   ○ B. adverb

9. The grazing deer came very <u>near</u>, and we tried not to move.
   ○ A. preposition   ○ B. adverb

Part 2 Identifying Prepositional Phrases   Identify the prepositional phrase in each sentence. (4 points each)

10. Yesterday Jerry found a quarter near the walkway.
    ○ A. found a quarter   ○ B. near the walkway   ○ C. Yesterday Jerry

11. Much later, we left without our coats.
    ○ A. Much later   ○ B. our coats   ○ C. without our coats

12. This toy was given to him and me long ago.
    ○ A. given to him   ○ B. to him and me   ○ C. long ago

Go to the next page.

13. Several members of the other team objected strongly.
 ○ A. of the other team ○ B. the other team ○ C. objected strongly

Part 3 Using Pronouns as Objects of Prepositions Choose the correct word to complete the sentence. (4 points each)

14. Evonne brought cookies made by her mother and _____.
 ○ A. she ○ B. her

15. The vote is between him and _____ for class president.
 ○ A. I ○ B. me

16. For _____ were you calling?
 ○ A. who ○ B. whom

17. Between his partner and _____ is a solid bond of trust.
 ○ A. him ○ B. he

Part 4 Identifying Adjective and Adverb Phrases Identify each underlined phrase as an adjective phrase or an adverb phrase. (4 points each)

18. The woman in the orange life jacket rowed expertly.
 ○ A. adjective phrase ○ B. adverb phrase

19. The pier stretched far beyond the shoreline.
 ○ A. adjective phrase ○ B. adverb phrase

20. The first ferry to the mainland sails at dawn.
 ○ A. adjective phrase ○ B. adverb phrase

21. My sister built a model of a circuit board.
 ○ A. adjective phrase ○ B. adverb phrase

Part 5 Identifying Conjunctions and Interjections Identify each conjunction or interjection. (4 points each)

22. Ducks and geese floated peacefully on the lake.
 ○ A. and ○ B. on ○ C. the

23. The town council must approve or disapprove of the proposed road.
 ○ A. must ○ B. or ○ C. of

24. Wow! That was the greatest concert I've attended.
 ○ A. Wow ○ B. attended ○ C. greatest

25. The storm struck the beach community fiercely but briefly.
 ○ A. the ○ B. beach ○ C. but

Using Compound and Complex Sentences

Part 1 Identifying Compound Sentences   Identify each of the following sentences as simple or compound. (4 points each)

1. The crew checked the ship and prepared it for sea.
   ● A. simple sentence   ○ B. compound sentence

2. We must repair the dam, or the water will rush through.
   ○ A. simple sentence   ● B. compound sentence

3. The people had voted and had chosen a new mayor.
   ● A. simple sentence   ○ B. compound sentence

4. The ducks arrived in early April and remained on the pond until October.
   ● A. simple sentence   ○ B. compound sentence

5. Tony scrubbed the kitchen floor, and his brother cleaned the basement.
   ○ A. simple sentence   ● B. compound sentence

6. We planned the picnic carefully, but the weather was very unpleasant.
   ○ A. simple sentence   ● B. compound sentence

7. My older sister or my cousin will call you tonight.
   ● A. simple sentence   ● B. compound sentence

8. My next-door neighbor has fine collections of butterflies and seashells.
   ○ A. simple sentence   ○ B. compound sentence

9. The police officer studied the map and decided on a new strategy.
   ● A. simple sentence   ○ B. compound sentence

10. The storm hit with fierce winds, but people were prepared for it.
    ○ A. simple sentence   ● B. compound sentence

Part 2 Punctuating Compound Sentences   Decide whether each of the following sentences is correctly or incorrectly punctuated. (4 points each)

11. The firefighters worked for two hours but the fire remained out of control.
    ○ A. correct   ● B. incorrect

12. A committee studied the problem; then it reported its findings to the town leaders.
    ● A. correct   ○ B. incorrect

Go to the next page.

13. We must tie these lines, or the boat will bump against the dock.
    ◉ A. correct   ○ B. incorrect

14. The winds died down; the clouds broke up.
    ○ A. correct   ○ B. incorrect

15. The jetliner first circled the field, then it landed from the south.
    ○ A. correct   ○ B. incorrect

16. My mother made a delicious salad, and my father grilled the fish perfectly.
    ○ A. correct   ○ B. incorrect

17. The sun dropped below the horizon night came quickly.
    ○ A. correct   ○ B. incorrect

18. The audience enjoyed the plot of the play, but the acting wasn't very good.
    ○ A. correct   ○ B. incorrect

19. You must meet the deadline, or your application will be rejected.
    ○ A. correct   ○ B. incorrect

20. My uncle hooked the fish, but he lost it soon afterward.
    ○ A. correct   ○ B. incorrect

Part 3 Identifying Compound and Complex Sentences   Identify each of the following sentences as compound or complex. (4 points each)

21. Nick must get here by five, or we will have to leave without him.
    ○ A. compound   ○ B. complex

22. After the rain ended, a rainbow arched across the sky.
    ○ A. compound   ◉ B. complex

23. The day was perfect for hiking, but the trails were not in good repair.
    ◉ A. compound   ○ B. complex

24. When Marcie had finished her painting, she stood back to admire it.
    ○ A. compound   ◉ B. complex

25. Lena never changes her mind once she has made a decision.
    ○ A. compound   ◉ B. complex

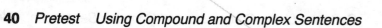

Using Compound and Complex Sentences

Part 1 Identifying Compound Sentences   Identify each of the following sentences as simple or compound. (2 points each)

1. We rushed to the station, but the train had already left.
   ○ A. simple sentence   ⊙ B. compound sentence

2. The committee should select Loren or Alexander.
   ⊙ A. simple sentence   ○ B. compound sentence

3. The gates open at 6:00 P.M., and the game begins at 7:30 P.M.
   ○ A. simple sentence   ⊙ B. compound sentence

4. A group of citizens founded and still supports this museum.
   ⊙ A. simple sentence   ○ B. compound sentence

5. The team must win tonight, or it cannot possibly make the playoffs.
   ○ A. simple sentence   ⊙ B. compound sentence

6. It was suddenly quiet; the eye of the storm was passing over us.
   ⊙ A. simple sentence ___   ⊙ B. compound sentence

In each sentence below, identify the parts that are joined by a conjunction. (2 points each)

7. Be part of the solution, or you will be part of the problem.
   ○ A. subjects   ⊛ B. sentences   ○ C. verbs

8. Her love of children and her interest in science led her to a career as a pediatrician.
   ⊛ A. subjects   ○ B. sentences   ○ C. verbs

9. Little kittens need care and attention every day.
   ○ A. subjects   ⊙ B. verbs   ○ C. objects

10. Police officers and rescue workers thoroughly searched the area.
   ⊛ A. subjects   ○ B. verbs   ○ C. sentences

11. We must replace the shingles, or the roof will certainly leak.
   ○ A. subjects   ⊛ B. sentences   ○ C. objects

12. A group of students identified and solved the problem.
   ○ A. subjects   ○ B. verbs   ○ C. objects

Go to the next page.

13. The project will be difficult, but many people will help us.
    ○ A. sentences   ○ B. verbs   ○ C. objects

Part 2 Punctuating Compound Sentences   Decide whether each of the following sentences is correctly or incorrectly punctuated. (4 points each)

14. The wind blasted against the windows, and the rain flooded in through the leaky roof.
    ○ A. correct   ○ B. incorrect

15. The new owners built a running track for horses; they also developed a grazing area for sheep.
    ○ A. correct   ○ B. incorrect

16. The large ship approached the dock; the tugboats nudged it gently.
    ○ A. correct   ○ B. incorrect

17. I would like volunteer work, but I am very busy on Saturday afternoons.
    ○ A. correct   ○ B. incorrect

18. We must refuel the generator, or it will stop in a few minutes.
    ○ A. correct   ○ B. incorrect

19. The book was interesting, and Ana read it quickly.
    ○ A. correct   ○ B. incorrect

20. Gardening is hard work, but it is very satisfying.
    ○ A. correct   ○ B. incorrect

In each sentence below, choose the word that should be followed by a comma or choose D if no comma is needed. (4 points each)

21. Order now and we will process and fill your request immediately.
    ○ A. now   ○ B. process   ○ C. request   ○ D. no comma

22. Sabrina had better hurry and get to the station or she will certainly miss the train.
    ○ A. hurry   ○ B. station   ○ C. certainly   ○ D. no comma

23. The city cleaned up this field and a local youth group planted trees and flowers.
    ○ A. this   ○ B. field   ○ C. trees   ○ D. no comma

24. Andy and Pedro auditioned for the show but neither of them got a part.
    ○ A. Andy   ○ B. auditioned   ○ C. show   ○ D. no comma

25. We could take the afternoon train or wait until tomorrow morning.
    ○ A. wait   ○ B. afternoon   ○ C. train   ○ D. no comma

26. The campers will sleep in tents or sleeping bags and they will be on the trail before dawn.
○ A. tents   ○ B. bags   ○ C. trail   ○ D. no comma

27. We should arrive this evening but the bad weather might delay us.
○ A. should   ○ B. evening   ○ C. bad   ○ D. no comma

Part 3 Using Compound Sentences   Decide which of the following pairs of sentences are related closely enough in thought to be joined to form a compound sentence. (4 points each)

28. The Grand Canyon attracts a lot of tourists. My brother took good pictures of the canyon.
○ A. related   ○ B. unrelated

29. The coach has called a practice for tomorrow. Everyone must be there.
○ A. related   ○ B. unrelated

30. Tomorrow's weather must be perfect. We will cancel the picnic.
○ A. related   ○ B. unrelated

31. I almost won the race. I became very tired during the last eighteen meters.
○ A. related   ○ B. unrelated

32. The lake is very rough today. Interesting plants grow under water.
○ A. related   ○ B. unrelated

33. Some people can do two things at once. I can't.
○ A. related   ○ B. unrelated

34. Ben likes to baby-sit. Yard work is a way to earn money.
○ A. related   ○ B. unrelated

Part 4 Identifying Main Clauses and Subordinate Clauses   Identify the underlined clause in each sentence as main or subordinate. (2 points each)

35. As long as you are here, <u>you can help us</u>.
○ A. main clause   ○ B. subordinate clause

36. Cory will not buy anything <u>unless he really needs it</u>.
○ A. main clause   ○ B. subordinate clause

37. <u>Because Lawana had a cold</u>, she decided to stay home.
○ A. main clause   ○ B. subordinate clause

Go to the next page.

38. <u>No one has seen Leland</u> since he got that computer.
○ A. main clause   ○ B. subordinate clause

39. <u>If you believe in yourself</u>, you can achieve great things.
○ A. main clause   ○ B. subordinate clause

40. Trish was cold, <u>so she turned up the thermostat</u>.
○ A. main clause   ○ B. subordinate clause

41. <u>The dog is barking</u> as if it wants to come in.
○ A. main clause   ○ B. subordinate clause

42. <u>Please try to wait</u> until we can get there.
○ A. main clause   ○ B. subordinate clause

Part 5 Identifying Compound and Complex Sentences   Identify each sentence as compound or complex. (2 points each)

43. Janet dropped a small tomato plant into the hole which Susan had just dug.
○ A. compound sentence   ○ B. complex sentence

44. Eat your soup now, or it will get cold.
○ A. compound sentence   ○ B. complex sentence

45. Jemina looks fragile, but she is actually quite strong.
○ A. compound sentence   ○ B. complex sentence

46. Wherever they settled, the pioneers cleared the land.
○ A. compound sentence   ○ B. complex sentence

47. The fields that I remember were always filled with clover.
○ A. compound sentence   ○ B. complex sentence

48. Maria knows the possible consequences of her decision, but she stands by it.
○ A. compound sentence   ○ B. complex sentence

49. Unless we get Ms. Zhang's approval, we will not proceed.
○ A. compound sentence   ○ B. complex sentence

50. The ski trip will take place in two weeks if we raise enough money by then.
○ A. compound sentence   ○ B. complex sentence

Understanding Subject and Verb Agreement

Part 1 Identifying Singular and Plural Forms Below each sentence, identify the noun or verb that is singular. (4 points each)

1. The path through the woods stays cool even on hot days.
   ○ A. woods   ○ B. stays   ○ C. cool   ○ D. days

2. Late in the day, the sun casts long shadows across the lawn.
   ○ A. in   ○ B. casts   ○ C. shadows   ○ D. across

3. One of the boys on the corner was in my class last year.
   ○ A. boys   ○ B. was   ○ C. in   ○ D. last

Below each sentence, identify the noun or verb that is plural. (4 points each)

4. Were the members of the team at the meeting last night?
   ○ A. Were   ○ B. team   ○ C. meeting   ○ D. night

5. The old desks in this room need much repair work.
   ○ A. room   ○ B. need   ○ C. much   ○ D. work

6. Some of the birds in our area are ready for the flight south.
   ○ A. our   ○ B. are   ○ C. ready   ○ D. flight

Part 2 Making Subjects and Verbs Agree Choose the correct verb to complete each sentence. (4 points each)

7. My dad _____ a great deal of shopping.
   ○ A. does   ○ B. do

8. The tiger_____ a member of the cat family.
   ○ A. is   ○ B. are

9. Several of my classmates _____ at the game last night.
   ○ A. was   ○ B. were

10. This old car _____ a lot of work.
   ○ A. needs   ○ B. need

11. The winner of several of the events _____ Peter.
   ○ A. was   ○ B. were

Go to the next page.

12. Usually I _____ the street two blocks west.
    ○ A. crosses   ○ B. cross

13. One of the bridges _____ washed away by the flood.
    ○ A. was   ○ B. were

14. Ted and I _____ always on time.
    ○ A. am   ○ B. are

15. Mai Ling and Claire _____ well on math tests.
    ○ A. does   ○ B. do

16. Neither Jack nor his brothers _____ very tall.
    ○ A. is   ○ B. are

17. The students themselves or their adviser _____ every field trip.
    ○ A. plans   ○ B. plan

18. One of my brothers or both brothers _____ waiting for me.
    ○ A. is   ○ B. are

19. Neither rain nor snow _____ kept me from delivering my papers.
    ○ A. has   ○ B. have

20. Here _____ the new softball league schedules.
    ○ A. is   ○ B. are

21. Where _____ this oversized book belong on the shelves?
    ○ A. does   ○ B. do

22. At this spot _____ six deer just five minutes ago.
    ○ A. was   ○ B. were

23. In the back of the room _____ three stacks of books.
    ○ A. was   ○ B. were

24. _____ there another mail delivery today?
    ○ A. Is   ○ B. Are

25. Around the corner _____ two ancient automobiles.
    ○ A. comes   ○ B. come

Understanding Subject and Verb Agreement

Part 1 Identifying Singular and Plural Forms   Identify the subject and verb of each sentence as either singular or plural. (4 points each)

1. Each clap of thunder makes the windows vibrate.
   - Ⓐ A. singular subject and verb
   - ◯ B. plural subject and verb

2. Matthew often climbs the four flights of stairs for exercise.
   - Ⓐ A. singular subject and verb
   - ◯ B. plural subject and verb

3. Not many vegetables are high in calories.
   - ◯ A. singular subject and verb
   - Ⓑ B. plural subject and verb

4. Is Bianca trying out for the part of the duchess?
   - Ⓐ A. singular subject and verb
   - ◯ B. plural subject and verb

5. In our town, many churches have beautiful, tall spires.
   - ◯ A. singular subject and verb
   - Ⓑ B. plural subject and verb

6. All those old movies run on the late, late show.
   - ◯ A. singular subject and verb
   - Ⓑ B. plural subject and verb

Part 2 Making Subjects and Verbs Agree   For each sentence, choose the correct form of the verb. (4 points each)

7. In fairy tales, the third son _____ almost always a hero.
   - Ⓐ A. is   ◯ B. are

8. Red tulips and a yellow bush _____ in bloom in our garden.
   - ◯ A. is   Ⓑ B. are

9. Either Jeff or his sister _____ the *Star Trek* reruns each week.
   - Ⓐ A. watches   ◯ B. watch

10. Above the wide river _____ countless fireworks.
    - ◯ A. explodes   ◯ B. explode

Go to the next page.

11. The employees of the new company _____ their work.
    ○ A. enjoys   ○ B. enjoy

12. Carol and her cousins _____ regularly every afternoon.
    ○ A. exercises   ○ B. exercise

13. Neither the banjo nor the guitars _____ exactly in tune.
    ○ A. seems   ○ B. seem

14. Where _____ the two horses from Bar-7 Stables?
    ○ A. is   ○ B. are

15. My two cousins or their mother _____ us in front of the library every
    Saturday.
    ○ A. meets   ○ B. meet

16. One of the teachers _____ every game.
    ○ A. supervises   ○ B. supervise

17. After four years, I _____ the oldest member of the troop.
    ○ A. am   ○ B. is

18. Without doubt, you _____ complete support from me.
    ○ A. has   ○ B. have

19. Here _____ the best basketball player in our school.
    ○ A. comes   ○ B. come

20. Various parts of this engine _____ daily maintenance.
    ○ A. needs   ○ B. need

21. Over the courthouse _____ the national and state flags.
    ○ A. flies   ○ B. fly

22. The supervisor of the town parks _____ a very good job.
    ○ A. does   ○ B. do

23. _____ everyone purchased a ticket?
    ○ A. Has   ○ B. Have

24. There _____ more than 500 species of animals in the city zoo.
    ○ A. is   ○ B. are

25. Either a person in a strange costume or a creature from space _____
    at our door.
    ○ A. is   ○ B. are

Capitalization

Part 1 Capitalizing Proper Nouns and Proper Adjectives In each
sentence, find the word or words that should be capitalized. (5 points each)

1. My cousin roger entered every cross-country event in last week's races.
   ○ A. Cousin   ○ C. Cross-Country
   ○ B. Roger   ○ D. Races

2. Among the heirlooms inherited from my grandfather was an old family bible.
   ○ A. Heirlooms   ○ B. Grandfather   ○ C. Family   ○ D. Bible

3. Fred and i found a shortcut through the woods and over the river.
   ○ A. I   ○ B. Shortcut   ○ C. Woods   ○ D. River

4. The main speaker after the banquet was my friend professor samuel miller.
   ○ A. Speaker   ○ C. Friend
   ○ B. Banquet   ○ D. Professor Samuel Miller

5. The lake is located just north of the town of hillsboro.
   ○ A. Lake   ○ B. North   ○ C. Town   ○ D. Hillsboro

6. Most cities of the northwest have a mild climate and many scenic attractions.
   ○ A. Cities   ○ B. Northwest   ○ C. Climate   ○ D. Attractions

7. The Sierra club is dedicated to preserving wildlife and conserving resources.
   ○ A. Club   ○ B. Wildlife   ○ C. Conserving   ○ D. Resources

8. Of all the national parks, yellowstone welcomes the most visitors each summer.
   ○ A. National Parks   ○ C. Visitors
   ○ B. Yellowstone   ○ D. Summer

9. Our high school was named after a hero who was a captain in world war II.
   ○ A. High School ○ B. Hero   ○ C. Captain   ○ D. World War

10. On Thursday evenings during the winter semester, mom works as a librarian.
    ○ A. Winter   ○ B. Semester   ○ C. Mom   ○ D. Librarian

11. A leadership conference is scheduled for the third and fourth weeks in june.
    ○ A. Leadership ○ B. Conference   ○ C. Weeks   ○ D. June

13. A train called the *crystal limited* leaves the main station once a week.

    ○ A. Train   ○ C. Main Station

    ○ B. *Crystal Limited*   ○ D. Week

14. The officials closed the old bridge at 5:00 a.m. because of an accident.

    ○ A. Officials   ○ B. Bridge   ○ C. A.M.   ○ D. Accident

Part 2 Capitalizing First Words and Titles   Choose the answer that shows capital letters correctly. (5 points each)

15. ○ A. My uncle said, "put that container of milk on the back porch."

    ○ B. My Uncle said, "put that container of milk on the back porch."

    ○ C. My uncle said, "Put that container of milk on the back porch."

16. ○ A. Many students are saving money for college.

    ○ B. many students are saving money for college.

    ○ C. Many students are saving money for College.

17. ○ A. dear Uncle Joe,

    ○ B. dear uncle Joe,

    ○ C. Dear Uncle Joe,

18. ○ A. Karen enjoyed reading *The Adventures of Sherlock Holmes.*

    ○ B. Karen enjoyed reading *The adventures of Sherlock Holmes.*

    ○ C. Karen enjoyed reading *The adventures of sherlock holmes.*

19. ○ A. Up from the meadows rich with corn,
           Clear in the cool september morn,
           The clustered spires of frederick stand
           Green-walled by the hills of Maryland.

    ○ B. Up from the meadows rich with corn,
           Clear in the cool September morn,
           The clustered spires of Frederick stand
           Green-walled by the hills of Maryland.

    ○ C. Up from the meadows rich with corn,
           Clear in the cool september morn,
           the clustered spires of Frederick stand
           Green-walled by the hills of Maryland.

20. ○ A. II. Constructing a Kite
           A. Measuring the materials
           B. Assembling the materials

    ○ B. II. Constructing a kite
           A. measuring the materials
           B. assembling the materials

    ○ C. II. Constructing a kite
           A. Measuring the materials
           B. Assembling the materials

Capitalization

Part 1 Capitalizing Proper Nouns and Proper Adjectives Choose the sentence in which proper nouns and proper adjectives are capitalized correctly. (6 points each)

1. ○ A. My uncle Andrew recently bought a new Buick.
   ○ B. My Uncle Andrew recently bought a new Buick.
   ○ C. My Uncle Andrew recently bought a new buick.

2. ○ A. Did Mother find a brochure on English furniture from the Victorian era?
   ○ B. Did Mother find a brochure on english furniture from the Victorian era?
   ○ C. Did Mother find a brochure on English furniture from the victorian era?

3. ○ A. The statue of liberty was one hundred years old on July 4, 1986.
   ○ B. The Statue of Liberty was one hundred years old on july 4, 1986.
   ○ C. The Statue of Liberty was one hundred years old on July 4, 1986.

4. ○ A. The *conway limited* left Chicago at 2:30 p.m.
   ○ B. The *Conway Limited* left Chicago at 2:30 p.m.
   ○ C. The *Conway Limited* left Chicago at 2:30 P.M.

5. ○ A. Most people leave the resort town of Spring lake right after labor day.
   ○ B. Most people leave the resort town of Spring Lake right after Labor Day.
   ○ C. Most people leave the Resort town of Spring Lake right after Labor Day.

6. ○ A. Our friend sheriff Quarles has been a police officer for fifteen years.
   ○ B. Our friend Sheriff Quarles has been a Police Officer for fifteen years.
   ○ C. Our friend Sheriff Quarles has been a police officer for fifteen years.

7. ○ A. Adina asked rabbi benjamin rosen to describe his trip to Israel.
   ○ B. Adina asked Rabbi Benjamin Rosen to describe his trip to Israel.
   ○ C. Adina asked Rabbi Benjamin Rosen to describe his trip to israel.

8. ○ A. Lang Hospital is one of the most advanced medical facilities in the South.
   ○ B. Lang hospital is one of the most advanced medical facilities in the south.
   ○ C. Lang Hospital is one of the most advanced Medical Facilities in the South.

Go to the next page.

College of the Ouachitas

9. ○ A. The Normans defeated the Saxons at the Battle of Hastings.
   ○ B. The Normans defeated the Saxons at the battle of hastings.
   ○ C. The normans defeated the saxons at the Battle of Hastings.

10. ○ A. Taylor high school is located three miles east of Interstate 2.
    ○ B. Taylor High School is located three miles east of Interstate 2.
    ○ C. Taylor High School is located three miles East of Interstate 2.

Part 2 Capitalizing First Words and Titles Choose the answer that shows capital letters used correctly. (8 points each)

11. ○ A. With best regards,
    ○ B. with best regards,
    ○ C. With Best Regards,

12. ○ A. Walter Lord wrote a book called *a Night to remember* about the sinking of the *Titanic.*
    ○ B. Walter Lord wrote a book called *A Night To Remember* about the sinking of the *Titanic.*
    ○ C. Walter Lord wrote a book called *A Night to Remember* about the sinking of the *Titanic.*

13. ○ A. "The only way to have a friend," said Emerson, "is to be one."
    ○ B. "the only way to have a friend," said Emerson, "is to be one."
    ○ C. "The only way to have a friend," said Emerson, "Is to be one."

14. ○ A. Wild was the day; the wintry sea
            moaned sadly on new england's strand,
        When first the thoughtful and the free,
            our fathers, trod the desert land.
    ○ B. Wild was the day; the wintry sea
            Moaned sadly on New England's strand,
        When first the thoughtful and the free,
            Our fathers, trod the desert land.
    ○ C. Wild was the day; the wintry sea
            moaned sadly on new England's strand,
        when first the thoughtful and the free,
            our fathers, trod the desert land.

15. ○ A. II. Planning a garden
            A. measuring the land
            B. sketching a plot
            C. selecting the seeds
    ○ B. II. Planning a Garden
            A. Measuring the Land
            B. Sketching a Plot
            C. Selecting the Seeds
    ○ C. II. Planning a garden
            A. Measuring the land
            B. Sketching a plot
            C. Selecting the seeds

Punctuation

Part 1 Using End Marks   Select the most appropriate end mark for each sentence. (4 points each)

1. What a day we've had
   ○ A. .   ○ B. ?   ◉ C. !

2. The lowest temperature ever recorded was in Antarctica in 1960
   ○ A. .   ○ B. ?   ◉ C. !

3. Turn left as soon as you come to the third traffic light
   ◉ A. .   ○ B. ?   ○ C. !

4. Couldn't you have informed us earlier
   ○ A. .   ◉ B. ?   ○ C. !

Part 2 Using Commas and Quotation Marks   Select the sentence that is punctuated correctly. (4 points each)

5. ◉ A. It is not far from here, but the bridge has been out for a month.
   ○ B. It is not far from here but the bridge has been out for a month.

6. ◉ A. We took the engine apart and cleaned all the important assemblies.
   ○ B. We took the engine apart, and cleaned all the important assemblies.

7. ○ A. Carla collects butterflies, seashells and postcards.
   ◉ B. Carla collects butterflies, seashells, and postcards.

8. ◉ A. No, I don't think that plan will work.
   ○ B. No I don't think that plan will work.

9. ◉ A. In the middle of winter, I really long for spring.
   ○ B. In the middle of winter I really long for spring.

10. ○ A. Help me pick the apples Jim, and you can have some of them.
    ◉ B. Help me pick the apples, Jim, and you can have some of them.

11. ◉ A. St. Helena, a remote island in the South Atlantic, has an interesting history.
    ○ B. St. Helena a remote island in the South Atlantic has an interesting history.

12. ○ A. My brother asked "Where does the race begin?"
    ◉ B. My brother asked, "Where does the race begin?"
    ○ C. My brother asked, "Where does the race begin"?

13. A. "That button," Jan pointed out, "controls the speed of the train."

    ○ B. "That button" Jan pointed out "controls the speed of the train."

    ○ C. "That button", Jan pointed out, "controls the speed of the train."

14. A. The Senate passed the bill on November 17, 1843.

    ○ B. The Senate passed the bill on November, 17, 1843.

15. A. My cousin now lives at 42 Ash Lane, Waycross Georgia.

    ○ B. My cousin now lives at 42 Ash Lane, Waycross, Georgia.

16. ○ A. After calling my mother left for work.

    B. After calling, my mother left for work.

Part 3 Using Semicolons, Colons, and Hyphens   Select the sentence that is punctuated correctly. (4 points each)

17. ○ A. The train came to a stop, the passengers began to board.

    B. The train came to a stop; the passengers began to board.

18. ○ A. In the morning, Tom and I picked peppers, strawberries, and beans, and Lauren and Judy picked peas, celery, and beets.

    B. In the morning, Tom and I picked peppers, strawberries, and beans; and Lauren and Judy picked peas, celery, and beets.

19. ○ A. We got everything together, brushes, paint, rags, rollers, and a large dropcloth.

    B. We got everything together: brushes, paint, rags, rollers, and a large dropcloth.

20. A. Dr. Abrams is a well-known biologist.

    ○ B. Dr. Abrams is a well known biologist.

21. A. The crew was in that small raft for twenty-five days.

    ○ B. The crew was in that small raft for twenty five days.

Part 4 Using Apostrophes   Select the correct contraction or possessive. (4 points each)

22. who is   ○ A. who'se   B. who's

23. would not   A. wouldn't   ○ B. would'nt

24. the grades of James   A. James's grades   ○ B. James' grades

25. a team of girls   ○ A. girl's team   B. girls' team

Punctuation

Part 1 Using End Marks   Select the most appropriate end mark for each sentence (5 points each)

1. Will the train for Detroit be on time
   ○ A. .   ◉ B. ?   ○ C. !

2. What a fantastic play that was
   ○ A. .   ○ B. ?   ◉ C. !

3. Let's meet at the library tonight
   ◉ A. .   ○ B. ?   ○ C. !

4. Sandra asked where the keys were
   ◉ A. .   ○ B. ?   ○ C. !

Part 2 Using Commas   Select the sentence that is punctuated correctly. (5 points each)

5. ◉ A. The water began to rise rapidly but never reached the three-foot mark.
   ○ B. The water began to rise rapidly, but never reached the three-foot mark.

6. ◉ A. We secured the doors early in the morning, and the police checked them for the rest of the day.
   ○ B. We secured the doors early in the morning and the police checked them for the rest of the day.

7. ○ A. A summer resort for years Darwin Beach is now a year-round community.
   ◉ B. A summer resort for years, Darwin Beach is now a year-round community.

8. ◉ A. The problem, Fred, is hard to solve.
   ○ B. The problem Fred is hard to solve.

9. ◉ A. December 31, 1999, will be a special New Year's Eve.
   ○ B. December 31, 1999 will be a special New Year's Eve.

10. ○ A. Karen now lives at 31 Bay Street, Fort Lauderdale, Florida for part of the year.
    ◉ B. Karen now lives at 31 Bay Street, Fort Lauderdale, Florida, for part of the year.

Part 3 Using Semicolons, Colons, and Hyphens   Select the sentence that is punctuated correctly. (5 points each)

11. ⊘ A. Todd pushed the button; the door opened immediately.
    ○ B. Todd pushed the button, the door opened immediately.

12. ⊘ A. Hilda Josephson is a well-respected judge, and she is also a well-known legal scholar.
    ○ B. Hilda Josephson is a well-respected judge, and she is also a well known legal scholar.

13. ⊘ A. We need the following supplies for the first-aid kit: bandages, cold packs, tape, scissors, gauze, and a thermometer.
    ○ B. We need the following supplies for the first-aid kit bandages, cold packs, tape, scissors, gauze, and a thermometer.

14. ⊘ A. My great-aunt is ninety-three years old.
    ○ B. My great aunt is ninety-three years old.

Part 4 Using Apostrophes   Choose the correct form of the possessive or contraction. (5 points each)

15. the records of the students
    ○ A. the student's records   ⊘ B. the students' records

16. the promise of Charles
    ⊘ A. Charles's promise   ○ B. Charles' promise

17. could not
    ⊘ A. couldn't   ○ B. could'nt

18. we are
    ○ A. wer'e   ⊘ B. we're

Part 5 Using Quotation Marks   Select the sentence that is punctuated correctly. (5 points each)

19. ⊘ A. "That," said Mai, "is the best throw of the game."
    ○ B. "That" said Mai "is the best throw of the game."
    ○ C. "That" said Mai, "is the best throw of the game."

20. ⊘ A. Mr. Anders said that he really enjoyed his vacation.
    ○ B. Mr. Anders said that "he really enjoyed his vacation."
    ○ C. Mr. Anders said, that "he really enjoyed his vacation."

Answer Sheet

Name _____ Date _____

Test _____ Score _____

Directions: Use your pencil to fill in the circle next to the correct answer for each test item. Be sure to fill in each circle completely.

1. ○ A ○ C   16. ○ A ○ C   31. ○ A ○ C   46. ○ A ○ C
   ○ B ○ D   ○ B ○ D   ○ B ○ D   ○ B ○ D

2. ○ A ○ C   17. ○ A ○ C   32. ○ A ○ C   47. ○ A ○ C
   ○ B ○ D   ○ B ○ D   ○ B ○ D   ○ B ○ D

3. ○ A ○ C   18. ○ A ○ C   33. ○ A ○ C   48. ○ A ○ C
   ○ B ○ D   ○ B ○ D   ○ B ○ D   ○ B ○ D

4. ○ A ○ C   19. ○ A ○ C   34. ○ A ○ C   49. ○ A ○ C
   ○ B ○ D   ○ B ○ D   ○ B ○ D   ○ B ○ D

5. ○ A ○ C   20. ○ A ○ C   35. ○ A ○ C   50. ○ A ○ C
   ○ B ○ D   ○ B ○ D   ○ B ○ D   ○ B ○ D

6. ○ A ○ C   21. ○ A ○ C   36. ○ A ○ C   51. ○ A ○ C
   ○ B ○ D   ○ B ○ D   ○ B ○ D   ○ B ○ D

7. ○ A ○ C   22. ○ A ○ C   37. ○ A ○ C   52. ○ A ○ C
   ○ B ○ D   ○ B ○ D   ○ B ○ D   ○ B ○ D

8. ○ A ○ C   23. ○ A ○ C   38. ○ A ○ C   53. ○ A ○ C
   ○ B ○ D   ○ B ○ D   ○ B ○ D   ○ B ○ D

9. ○ A ○ C   24. ○ A ○ C   39. ○ A ○ C   54. ○ A ○ C
   ○ B ○ D   ○ B ○ D   ○ B ○ D   ○ B ○ D

10. ○ A ○ C   25. ○ A ○ C   40. ○ A ○ C   55. ○ A ○ C
    ○ B ○ D   ○ B ○ D   ○ B ○ D   ○ B ○ D

11. ○ A ○ C   26. ○ A ○ C   41. ○ A ○ C   56. ○ A ○ C
    ○ B ○ D   ○ B ○ D   ○ B ○ D   ○ B ○ D

12. ○ A ○ C   27. ○ A ○ C   42. ○ A ○ C   57. ○ A ○ C
    ○ B ○ D   ○ B ○ D   ○ B ○ D   ○ B ○ D

13. ○ A ○ C   28. ○ A ○ C   43. ○ A ○ C   58. ○ A ○ C
    ○ B ○ D   ○ B ○ D   ○ B ○ D   ○ B ○ D

14. ○ A ○ C   29. ○ A ○ C   44. ○ A ○ C   59. ○ A ○ C
    ○ B ○ D   ○ B ○ D   ○ B ○ D   ○ B ○ D

15. ○ A ○ C   30. ○ A ○ C   45. ○ A ○ C   60. ○ A ○ C
    ○ B ○ D   ○ B ○ D   ○ B ○ D   ○ B ○ D

Answer Key

Handbook 37 Understanding Sentences

Pretest
Pages 7–8

1. B	6. C	11. C	16. B
2. A	7. A	12. C	17. B
3. A	8. B	13. C	18. C
4. C	9. A	14. A	19. A
5. B	10. A	15. A	20. C

Mastery Test
Pages 9–12

1. A	10. A	19. A	28. C
2. B	11. B	20. D	29. B
3. C	12. B	21. C	30. A
4. C	13. A	22. B	31. B
5. B	14. B	23. A	32. C
6. C	15. B	24. B	33. B
7. A	16. A	25. A	34. A
8. B	17. B	26. C	35. C
9. B	18. A	27. A	

Handbook 38 Using Nouns

Pretest
Pages 13–14

1. B	6. C	11. C	16. B
2. B	7. A	12. D	17. C
3. C	8. B	13. C	18. B
4. D	9. A	14. A	19. C
5. D	10. B	15. C	20. A

Mastery Test
Pages 15–16

1. B	6. B	11. B	16. B
2. C	7. A	12. A	17. A
3. A	8. B	13. A	18. B
4. A	9. C	14. A	19. A
5. A	10. B	15. C	20. C

Handbook 39 Using Pronouns

Pretest
Pages 17–18

1. A	8. B	15. B	22. B
2. C	9. B	16. B	23. A
3. A	10. B	17. B	24. B
4. B	11. A	18. A	25. B
5. A	12. B	19. C	
6. A	13. B	20. B	
7. A	14. A	21. A	

Mastery Test
Pages 19–22

1. A	14. B	27. B	40. B
2. B	15. B	28. A	41. A
3. C	16. A	29. A	42. B
4. B	17. B	30. B	43. A
5. B	18. A	31. A	44. A
6. C	19. B	32. A	45. A
7. B	20. A	33. B	46. A
8. A	21. B	34. B	47. B
9. A	22. A	35. B	48. A
10. B	23. A	36. B	49. B
11. B	24. A	37. B	50. A
12. B	25. B	38. A	
13. A	26. A	39. A	

Handbook 40 Using Verbs

Pretest
Pages 23–24

1. B	8. B	15. B	22. B
2. A	9. A	16. C	23. B
3. B	10. B	17. B	24. A
4. B	11. B	18. A	25. A
5. A	12. A	19. A	
6. A	13. B	20. B	
7. A	14. A	21. B	

Mastery Test
Pages 25–26

1. A	6. A	11. B	16. B
2. B	7. B	12. B	17. B
3. C	8. B	13. C	18. A
4. B	9. C	14. C	19. B
5. B	10. C	15. B	20. B

Handbook 41 Using Adjectives

Pretest
Pages 27–28

1. B	6. A	11. B	16. C
2. A	7. A	12. A	17. B
3. C	8. B	13. C	18. C
4. B	9. A	14. B	19. B
5. B	10. B	15. B	20. C

Mastery Test
Pages 29–30

1. A	8. B	15. B	22. B
2. B	9. C	16. C	23. B
3. B	10. B	17. B	24. C
4. C	11. A	18. C	25. A
5. B	12. C	19. B	
6. B	13. B	20. C	
7. C	14. C	21. A	

Handbook 42 Using Adverbs

Pretest
Pages 31–32

1. C	8. B	15. B	22. B
2. A	9. A	16. A	23. A
3. C	10. A	17. A	24. B
4. B	11. B	18. A	25. A
5. D	12. A	19. B	
6. B	13. A	20. B	
7. C	14. B	21. A	

Mastery Test

Pages 33–34

1. C	6. A	11. B	16. B
2. A	7. B	12. B	17. B
3. B	8. C	13. A	18. A
4. A	9. B	14. B	19. B
5. D	10. A	15. A	20. A

Handbook 43 Using Prepositions, Conjunctions, and Interjections

Pretest

Pages 35–36

1. B	8. A	15. A	22. C
2. B	9. B	16. A	23. C
3. C	10. C	17. B	24. A
4. B	11. B	18. A	25. B
5. C	12. B	19. B	
6. B	13. B	20. A	
7. A	14. B	21. B	

Mastery Test

Pages 37–38

1. B	8. A	15. B	22. A
2. A	9. B	16. B	23. B
3. C	10. B	17. A	24. A
4. C	11. C	18. A	25. C
5. C	12. B	19. B	
6. B	13. A	20. B	
7. A	14. B	21. A	

Handbook 44 Using Compound and Complex Sentences

Pretest

Pages 39–40

1. A	8. A	15. B	22. B
2. B	9. A	16. A	23. A
3. A	10. B	17. B	24. B
4. A	11. B	18. A	25. B
5. B	12. A	19. A	
6. B	13. A	20. A	
7. A	14. A	21. A	

Mastery Test

Pages 41–44

1. B	14. B	27. B	40. B
2. A	15. A	28. B	41. A
3. B	16. A	29. A	42. A
4. A	17. A	30. A	43. B
5. B	18. B	31. A	44. A
6. B	19. B	32. B	45. A
7. B	20. A	33. A	46. B
8. A	21. A	34. B	47. B
9. C	22. B	35. A	48. A
10. A	23. B	36. B	49. B
11. B	24. C	37. B	50. B
12. B	25. D	38. A	
13. A	26. B	39. B	

Handbook 45 Understanding Subject and Verb Agreement

Pretest

Pages 45–46

1. B	8. A	15. B	22. B
2. B	9. B	16. B	23. B
3. B	10. A	17. A	24. A
4. A	11. A	18. B	25. B
5. B	12. B	19. A	
6. B	13. A	20. B	
7. A	14. B	21. A	

Mastery Test

Pages 47–48

1. A	8. B	15. A	22. A
2. A	9. A	16. A	23. A
3. B	10. B	17. A	24. B
4. A	11. B	18. B	25. A
5. B	12. B	19. A	
6. B	13. B	20. B	
7. A	14. B	21. B	

Handbook 46 Capitalization

Pretest

Pages 49–50

1. B	6. B	11. D	16. A
2. D	7. A	12. C	17. C
3. A	8. B	13. B	18. A
4. D	9. D	14. C	19. B
5. D	10. C	15. C	20. C

Mastery Test

Pages 51–52

1. B	5. B	9. A	13. A
2. A	6. C	10. B	14. B
3. C	7. B	11. A	15. C
4. C	8. A	12. C	

Handbook 47 Punctuation

Pretest

Pages 53–54

1. C	8. A	15. B	22. B
2. A	9. A	16. B	23. A
3. A	10. B	17. B	24. A
4. B	11. A	18. B	25. B
5. A	12. B	19. B	
6. A	13. A	20. A	
7. B	14. A	21. A	

Mastery Test

Pages 55–56

1. B	6. A	11. A	16. A
2. C	7. B	12. A	17. A
3. A	8. A	13. A	18. B
4. A	9. A	14. A	19. A
5. A	10. B	15. B	20. A